CW00392165

AURO

SUMMER SOLSTICE 2023

HOMECOMING

AUROCHS UNDERGROUND PRESS

Aurochs 1: Homecoming

ISBN 978-1-7396972-3-5

Published by Aurochs Underground Press, Bath, UK

HOMECOMING

A Journal of New Animist Writing

EDITED BY JACK WOLF

LIST OF ARTWORKS:

Maria Strutz:

Carrie Osborne:

HOMECOMING

CONTENTS :

HOMECOMING

Graham Harvey

INTRODUCTION

I'm sitting by a window, looking out (when I'm not looking at my computer screen) across the valley of the South Tyne river. The snow that fell in the last hour is melting fast along the Stanegate, the road our garden gate opens on to. The road has been here, more or less, since the Romans or before, but has a Saxon name. The melting snow is cooling the soil in the raised beds so I've not planted out the vegetable seedlings yet. Our neighbours have put food out for birds – although they don't welcome the jays. On the wall above my computer are paintings and photos of special places in Northumberland, Wiltshire and the central desert of Australia. They tell me stories. I could tell you stories. Or I could if I was a story-teller like those whose work is gathered in the pages that follow.

I've just deleted some words that began "Those stories are about". I deleted my words not only because it is not my role to summarise what follows. I deleted them mostly because stories cannot, must not be reduced to short sentences. Short sentences can tell big stories. But stories cannot, must not be made to say only one thing. Even only one good thing.

So, I'll try to do what I think I was invited to do. That is to say something about some of the big, eloquent story-words to which the word-smithing that follows are responses. Those key words (unlocking words of power) are animism and Indigenous. Wonderful wonder-full acts of serendipity and of generous hosting have taken me to places (always communities, never only of humans) in which I have learnt some things about those words and the lives and relations they evoke. I have learnt that the stories these words introduce are about becoming, doing, interacting, relating. They work best when they inspire verbs rather than nouns.

Animism was once a term of abuse. It still is, sometimes. It alleged that a mistake keeps being made in which people (human people in this case) failed to distinguish humans from other existences. Modern people are supposed to know the difference. More accurately, Modernity is about teaching and learning the difference. It does not come naturally to anyone. No surprise there. It involves an act of violence to assert or accept that the world around us only has value because humans give it meaning. Or that there is a realm of "nature" separate from "culture". That is a story that has made the world we now live in. The world that is endangered by the story.

Animism has been reclaimed to tell another story. Many other words have been reclaimed to enable new stories that expand justice, respect, decency, possibility, hope. None of these words change the world when they are only said once or twice… They need repetition and drama before the old stories begin to lose their power. The colonial story wrapped up in the older use of animism is far from being over. I've been told by more than one Indigenous friend that this is not a post-colonial era but a most-colonial one. That's a heart-breaking, gut-wrenching true tale too. But if we keep speaking "animism" in a new way, that too might change.

I once wrote that animism, the new animism, is an understanding that the world is full of persons, only some of whom are human, and all of whom deserve respect. I'd learnt that (not the precise words but the vision) from Mi'kmaq and Anishinaabeg in what is now called North America. It wasn't a new discovery or a new story, not even among academics. There were already some powerful books and articles available to inspire new thinking and becoming. Also, it wasn't only the humans who told the story that inspired my efforts to sum up this "new animism".

I'd been at a conference and then a powwow in Miawpukek, the Mi'kmaq reserve by the Conne River in Newfoundland. As the final honour song was being danced by elders and veterans, the largest of the eagles who live by the Conne River flew a perfect circle over and around the drum group. Everyone recognised this as a special, powerful statement by the eagle. People are still talking about the flight of that kitpu, eagle, now. In one gracious glorious flight, the effort of an Indigenous community to return more fully to doing tradition, restoring sovereignty and expanding mutual aid was affirmed and encouraged. More than one person there told me "the birds, animals, fish and plants have kept tradition, and the eagle was saying 'glad you are joining in again'".

For a variety of reasons, "animism" has been reclaimed as a key word opening up respectful understanding of just such encounters, experiences, responses. One word doesn't tell the whole story. Indeed, it might misdirect the story. For example, it still leads people to imagine the big issue is a difference between life and death. Is this rock alive or dead? Is this scenery animate or inanimate? Some people think that humans are unique or even exceptional. They don't think the eagle was deliberately communicating anything. They're stuck in those old "Natural History" documentaries where "nature" is a place without humans (or maybe without white humans).

Tradition and kinship are words that can and do replace "animism" in many discussions of this kind. And this animism is not alien to "Western" worldviews or scholarship. Really it isn't. Darwin sketched human kinship with/in the larger-than-human community as part of his story of evolution. The phrase "all our relations" could be Darwin's as much as it is a refrain in Lakota originated sweat-lodges. I still like the phrase "other-than-human persons" because it provokes people to think differently about what makes someone a person rather than a thing. A "who" rather than a "what". And no longer just an "it". "Other-than-human" doesn't privilege humans – especially when there are stories about "other-than-bears" or "other-than-rocks" meeting other kinds of person. Talking about "kin" can do a similar job. We live our lives with others. Always. Inescapably. Integrally. But perhaps not always justly or ethically.

Animism is not a bland statement of fact: "we are all related". It is an evocation of efforts to live better with our kin. It involves not only sociology (what kind of community is this?) but also ethics (how do we improve our communities?). It involves responsibilities and requires commitments. Children might be animistic to some degree (easily chatting with cats and tables). But a life lived long and well (what Anishinaabeg call "bimaadiziwin") can increase the animism of elders. They learn locally appropriate etiquettes for engaging with others. They practice respect and gift-exchange. And much more.

Much more. But this isn't going to become a book length discussion. It mustn't get in the way of the stories, poems and other gifts that follow. So, to sum up the story so far: animism is a word that means "being a person is not given; it is a process, a becoming, a project". Learning to become more engaged with the communities among whom we live entails practising respect, listening, paying

10

attention, and giving thanks. As the poet Gary Snyder says "performance is currency in the deep world's gift economy". Songs, dances, ceremonies and other arts of living are among the ways we participate in the larger-than-human world. They are ways of acting-out our kinship and belonging. (Don't mistake those for givens, they too are projects, practices, stuff to learn to do better, verbs not nouns, ambitions.)

Indigenous. This is another hard-working word. And another ambition word. If it is an identity it is one people grow into. You may have noticed that I used a capital "I" earlier when I could have just typed "indigenous". Sometimes even one letter tells a story. Everything is "indigenous" somewhere – everything comes from somewhere. Chickens and oranges originate in southeast Asia. I come from Wiltshire. These facts do not matter very much. A bit, but they are not the same as the term "Indigenous" with a capital. Or, in fact, in ways of speaking about indigeneity with or without a capital. When Anishinaabeg, Huichol, Māori, Sámi or Yoruba speak about their indigeneity, they mean more than "coming from somewhere" or "belonging in". Indigenous in this context is an assertion of sovereignty and the rights and responsibilities of communities to self-define and self-govern. It is a strategic or political term. It is also, therefore, a comparative term. If there are Indigenous people or nations, there must be non-Indigenous or other-than-Indigenous people or nations. Principally, it is colonial people and nations who are, by definition, not Indigenous. Even if they are living in places where their ancestors always lived. The project of Modernity is a colonial one and the project of Indigeneity is a resistance movement. Not the only such movement – and that's important.

That might not satisfy everyone. But it is not the whole story. Indigenous people are often remarkably generous. While busy trying to build just, decent and sovereign communities – often with strongly ecological (multi-species kinship) ambitions – and often in the face of ongoing racism, violence, pollution and poverty – they frequently engage positively with other people. Plenty of Indigenous authors (academics, poets, novelists, futurists, essayists and legislators) keep saying that it is not their job to save the world, to teach better spirituality, better ecology, better anything. It must be particularly annoying when people want these things to be "authentic" – usually meaning "indigenous" in the sense of "fixed in the past, back in earlier times". Nonetheless, despite all that, Indigenous people are at the forefront of some of the best, most exciting cultural and scientific projects. They demonstrate that this is a "world in which many worlds are possible" as the Zapatistas say. Not all those worlds are just or sustainable. That's one reason for learning about the worlds that Indigenous and other people are composing, composting, nurturing or contesting.

In short, none of this means that there is no place for other-than-Indigenous people in these world-making (worlding) projects. It might, then, be helpful to state clearly that while not everyone can be Indigenous, everyone can indigenize. We can, perhaps must, find or make better ways of living in place/communities (places are always multi-species communities, as are bodies – say hello to elbow and gut bacteria). The slogan "think globally, act locally" is a form of indigenizing. We do not live on a small blue-green marble in a vast dark space. We are members of communities who make up the flows of life *in* earth. Anyone, everyone, everywhere can learn to listen to the conversations going on all around us.

At first, given the deep disjunctions caused by trying to be Modern, trying to be human separatists, telling ourselves a story about a world full of meaningless if entertaining non-humans, it'll take time to do more than

12

listen-in. It'll take time to demonstrate that we wish to belong, to join in, to contribute. Why should the birds acknowledge our presence? What are we doing that indicates that we want to be part of the community again? My suspicion is that the people whose work fills this book can tell stories like the one about the eagle at Miawpukek. They will recognise Snyder's "performance is currency" in celebrating gifts given and received. In the basket of writing that follows there will be some sweet and some bitter tastes.

Thomas King's book, *The Truth About Stories* (University of Minnesota Press, 2003) – and the recording of these as lectures you can easily find online – tell us that "the truth about stories is that that's all we are". In the world in which many worlds are possible, some stories are more just, more ecological, more likely to inspire us to act respectfully. We all know how disempowering, dis-motivating the stories of ecological disaster, climate collapse and mass extinction can be. They are necessary stories, true stories. But we also need stories of eagles encouraging ceremonies of respect. We need tales that celebrate local rivers and the eels, otters and kingfishers who make them a community. We need stories that take us to futures in which the resistance has succeeded. We need stories that change everything. Stories that live (because they too are animist) and, so, can be retold, adapted, adjusted and fitted for new situations and contexts (because they too are indigenizing).

13

Beth Mann

CARTA DE AMOR

When I first came here, we weren't on speaking terms. In those early days – days so hot that I thought my skin would peel away, and my eyes ached – I wasn't ready for talking. Too much baggage from the ex, too many memories. Moorland, hung with cloud, a skirling stream the only guide through mist and long grass. Sunlight glancing off chalk as I wandered among a circle of stones, beech tree shadows rippling over the warm ground. They made my stomach dive like a hawk, these memories, swoop with love.

With you, I felt nothing. Your sun-raddled face was blank; you stared straight back at me, unyielding. Summer-fettered, you had retreated into yourself, nothing but withered stalks and dust. We were not friends. Hardly even acquaintances. More like two creatures facing each other, hackles up, waiting to bare teeth. We both knew I did not belong.

Love takes time to ease, and love takes time to grow.

If you uproot a tree, it will cling with all its strength to the earth where it was born. Like a sappy, stripling birch, I carried home with me; not as a shower of dirt, nor a plump white grub wriggling in a web of roots. Not grit, not even a wisp of grass. Home came with me wrapped up in

14

a neat package, unsuspicious. This is the way to take home through airport security. Dirt tends to attract attention.

Home was cured deerskin, and the feather of a crow moulted among standing stones and left, shining sleek as obsidian in the Dartmoor rains. Chips of jasper foraged, once upon a time, with joy and trepidation, from a river in the borderlands. Feather of pigeon. A curving, dappled branch, cut from some leafy woodland of the south. You eyed me sideways as I shook that rattle around my new house, and you turned away. Or perhaps I turned away from you. Perhaps I wasn't ready, just then, to let go. To give my heart to someone else.

I don't know when we first started to talk. In the autumn, perhaps, when you were opening up with fresh growth, and the air was drowsy with your aromatic perfume; wild thyme, the piquant scent of olive bark. Seasons were turned upside down with you. Fiery beetles scuttled across your skin, making you flush. Larks danced in an azure sky. At night, in the warm darkness, owls drifted over my head, by day transmogrified into fierce red kites that made my heart cry with joy. You began to speak, and I began to listen.

I wanted to understand you. I scrabbled up pieces of you to take home, to bring you into my own space. Scavenged bones, rocks, feathers. Anything to bring me closer to you. You offered me the sooty plume from a stork; a perfect pine cone; a stone in the shape of an egg. Things to make me wrap my arms around you.

One day, they planted young cypress trees, down by the Roman road. I'd forgotten how red you are, when you're cut. How old, old you are. Pot sherds and rocks, man's time and land's time. Up in the cliffs there are fluted shells, thin as paper, memories of when you were sunk beneath oceans.

You carry so much. When the wind soughs through the pot-bellied olive trees, their bones creak and groan. Your

15

cliffs have stood, blank-faced, until the time of men. The Romans chipped away at you, then the Arabs, and now graffiti covers you, like make up poorly done. You're littered with broken bottles. Condoms lurk in the grass, and the earth is stained with ash. You stand through it all. I want to stand shoulder to shoulder with you. I lay the palm of my hand on the cliffs, feel the grit nip my skin. You're right to be wary, to show your teeth. You, too, have a love long lost.

I think the rain helps you to remember. After rain, you seem young again. Your flesh softens. Finches teem in the olive trees. Grasshoppers, thick and long as my finger, blunder about. The hoopoes flash from branch to branch. Maybe it reminds you of a time when you were understood.

Understanding, like love, comes slowly. I'm not sure I understand you truly, as hard as I try. I doubt you understand me. But you accept me. I won't forget my old love, and you know it. They're still there, waiting. Trees festooned with fog on an autumn morning. Rock-scattered moors. The blinding white chalk, covering my shoes in dusty kisses. They'll always be waiting. But here, now, I have you. And though you might not know it – you have me.

Winter is past. The time of equal day and night is here; we can feel it in our bones. Above us, falcons and storks circle on the thermals, and the swallows are arrows. Green fields stretch to the horizon. The air is perfumed with the musky sweetness of orange blossom. A new year is starting.

Let's see where this goes.

HOMECOMING

Arie Farnam

THE RIDGE

My family came to this homestead like refugees from a world threatening suicide. They had little money, but somehow, they put a down payment on 20 acres of dry, rocky land on a low ridge in the Blue Mountains of Eastern Oregon in 1975. *This thin-soiled, east-facing slope with a hundred-year-old, hand-dug, stone-lined well sixty feet deep. A few aged cherry trees from a time before the large, sugar-packed fruits of today. Some fir, less pine. Camas and biscuit root.*

While I slept - curled in the darkness of amniotic fluid - Mama, Pa and one-year-old Nat moved into the loft of an antique one-room schoolhouse on the neighbor's land. They meant to ride out the winter in that shelter and then build a cabin in the spring. But one night just after the winter solstice, the bone-dry wooden schoolhouse burnt to the ground. They were outside and no one was hurt, but they lost everything - the few photos of my parents' childhoods, clothes, dishes, tools - everything but the land.

The last material connections to previous generations went up in smoke. We had been severed from grandparents by trauma, abuse, mental illness, massive social change and the mental sicknesses of racism and colonialism. My uncles had no children and my only aunt fled as far away as it is possible to get while still remaining on the earth.

After that fire, there was the prospect of a new start. Not a clean start per se. Their hands were covered with soot and the smell of burning. But it was a start as fresh as springtime in the mountains.

In April, I was born in the sleeping nook of the shack they built in the snow up on the remnants of a broken-down flatbed truck next to the old well. I grew like a birch sapling on the edge of an unstable embankment, roots exposed to wind and water, clinging to eroding soil and crumbling stone. I remember no time before I knew that the land did not truly belong to me or I to it.

My parents were vaguely conscious of the genocide that had occurred here. And our "church" was the ridgetop. Our "preacher" was the meadowlark. They taught me respect for the land, for the trees and grasses, for the wild things, for the people who had been there before us. But mostly they were focused on our survival - gardens, livestock, how to pay the electric bill.

I knew there was something off in our connection to the land, even before I could understand half of those things. In the first six years, I came to know our relations and neighbors on the land with the uneasy sensibility of a poor cousin come to stay in a time of crisis. A child must be taught that the spring irises planted by some frontier woman a hundred years ago and the fir tree towering over the cabin that speaks in the wind and the mortar and pestle dug up in the camas field are not people. I was not taught these things very early. My mother did not teach them. She taught uncertainty and listening.

In my earliest memories, there is no loneliness. There were friends made of sunlight and tall grass and cool miner's lettuce and cows and dogs and frogs and a muddy pond. There were stories made up with a brother about a tree man who followed us through the woods and warned us away from danger.

There was the well itself. That narrow dark hole in the earth with water at the bottom set my family apart from our human neighbors. While others on the ridge hauled drinking and washing water in plastic barrels, we had a nearly endless supply of cold, slightly murky, woods-tasting well water.

Even as a little child, I didn't need to be told to give thanks to the well. But in my gratitude, I feared her dark, deep-mouthed presence under the pantry floor at the back of our cabin. I thought I saw glowing orange eyes there on nights when Nat and I washed the dinner dishes by the dim light of a single bulb. I couldn't see the shining eyes of cats and coyotes in the dark. I had been born with extremely poor eyesight, but this image appeared unbidden in my mind and stayed.

When I was fifteen, still slight and whip-strong, my father needed insulation to be tucked around the stone at the bottom of the well for a new pump to be installed. It was a job for someone with small shoulders, quick hands and no particular need to see much in the dark. I was well accustomed to doing things without much sight. He gave me a headlamp - though I could scarcely see shadows by its light - and instructions on what exactly to do (and not do) once I got to the bottom of the well.

Then he lowered me into her mouth on a rope, down the long narrow shaft to where the air smelled of old, old, damp stone. I sensed the massive weight of the tons of earth around me and my throat closed in instinctive fear. I fought it back, focused and did my task.

"Tug on the rope when you're done," he had said. "Don't shout whatever you do. And don't look up."

I tugged. I understood about not shouting. The fear of some stone vibrating loose from a loud noise to fall down on my head was more than enough to ensure my obedience. But there was a pause. A long pause and I couldn't resist the impulse. I glanced up for just a second.

Dislocation.

I could not fathom it. My thoughts scrambled. *Night. The moon.* A big, pale full moon rode in the utter darkness of night.

Then, *terror...* as I realized *that* was *not* the moon... but *her mouth,* the opening of the well.

I had imagined - as I kept my eyes down and completed my task at the bottom of the well - that if I looked up, I would see a long shaft and the opening I had come through - big enough for me, a little tight for Pa. *Three feet wide.*

But sixty feet of perspective had shrunk that hole to the size of the moon in the sky. The realization of my utter vulnerability so far beneath rock and soil gave me a shock of primal fear that quickly turned to awe and respect, as I swallowed the impulse to cry out and let myself be hauled - still and peaceful - out of the well.

I believe she was the first spirit being I came to know consciously. It seemed that I could point out the direction back to her, even if I was led by circuitous paths through the mountains, even if others who could see with their eyes were lost. My sense of direction was remarked as "uncanny" by sighted people, and if I thought about it when closer to home, that homing sense pointed, not at the door of the shack or even to the kitchen table where we ate, did homework, laughed and bickered... rather it pointed to the well.

She was not only a nurturing mother and provider, but also our subtle protector. Later in life, as I traveled through many countries, other travelers quickly fell sick drinking local water, while the voice of the old well whispered health and immunity in my veins.

In an arid land, the well makes the homestead. Those places that could not drill wells have all been abandoned. But our well was special because of the rock walls, those careful stones, row upon row which I saw down there in the earth. And feeding the well, there is a spring.

As awe-inspiring as the well is, the spirit of the spring is far older. Tucked among the fir trees half-way up the ridge, where two shoulders come together in a brushy draw, a bit of clear water - tasting of moss and stone - burbles out of the ground for a few months of the year. By midsummer it has retreated underground, though it still feeds the well.

A few yards to the south of the spring, there is a patch of "false white sage," a type of mugwort used for a cleansing smudge. Here, surrounded by tall fir, tamarack and pine, between the mule's ear, yarrow and paintbrush, this patch of a sacred plant hangs on, though it is not found on most of the ridge.

The image of a Numipu or Cayuse elder camped by the spring, burning a bundle of the herb and dropping a

20

few seeds into the loam of the forest floor, is so strong and sudden in my mind that I am sure it happened. The spring has a voice and a consciousness. And alongside it - closely tied to it - there is a human ancestral spirit, but one who has reason to see me and my family as intruders.

For many years, the rift between us and the spirits of our home was little more than a troubling whisper. As a teenager, I left this land and went across the ocean to the Czech lands in Central Europe - rich in ancient rocks and marshes. There the ridgelines were softer. Water was abundant, even to the point of frequent flooding. The trees tended toward oak, willow and linden. The flowers mostly had names, smells and voices I had to learn like a lesson in school. They did not come easy and natural to my high-desert senses.

But over the years, I did learn. In that wet land, I learned to be with the spirits of springs and waterways, to speak to them, to listen, to give offerings. I was a foreigner to them, but welcome because of my respect. The old animist customs were almost forgotten there as well, but not quite. There are still stories of the Vodník in Bohemia, the old man of ponds and waterwheels - *Green skin with a pointed beard and a long pipe.* Only whispers remain of Mokoš, lady of the spring or well, but often chapels or shrines were built by the holy wells with the names of female saints who carry on her watch.

Twenty-five years trickled away, like a swift flowing stream, and circumstances conspired to send me reeling back to my home place. I left the country of rolling hills and deciduous forests and returned to the big round valley, the high blue mountains speckled with snow, the rocky ridges and the dryland plants. The scent of them greets me with such overwhelming fragrance that my nose stings with the pungent spice of pine, sage, yarrow, juniper, fir, balsam root and just a tangy hint of larkspur and lupin.

I came back after a quarter century to kneel by the spring in the mugwort patch to beg forgiveness, and with it, asylum. My parents' world seemed on the verge of self-

21

destruction when I was born. I have no doubt that their concern was genuine and well-founded, despite the fact that the world is still here. Today, while it appears that immediate nuclear annihilation is less likely, there is a sense of an unstoppable, slow slide into desperation. And I am a blind woman as well as a failed high-competition journalist with two disabled kids adopted from Eastern European orphanages. I crawl back to the land of my birth and tug at the mother's tattered garments and cry for protection and succor.

At first, the watcher at the spring is quiet. She or he does not turn me away but nor am I immediately welcomed as a long-lost grandchild. *Why did I leave? Do I truly accept that the land does not belong to me, that land cannot be owned, that all these are persons?*

I walk up the old trail toward the open ridgetop, along the path lined with red, yellow and orange paintbrush, up to where the rocks come through the thin skin of the earth like bony shoulders. I cross another dry creek bed and walk among the bunch grass and scrub to a lone pine I know as well as any member of my family. We have always called her "the Umbrella Tree" though her shape is not as broad as all that. The name comes mostly from the sheltered, hollow space beneath her branches, which reach all the way to the ground.

There I played and Mama hid gifts for us. There my brothers' children grew and flourished. There I brought my own deeply wounded children to seek healing and protection in our time of great need. This grandmother pine tree has seen six hundred wind-blasted, snow-driven winters and six hundred hard-baked, sun-scorched summers.

She's overlooked the valley where the Cayuse, Numipu, Walla Walla, Umatilla and many others came for counsels of peace - their repeated attempts to stop wars and violence. She almost certainly saw women and girls spread out across the high meadow, digging camas and biscuit root. She saw children collecting dark berries in the shade of the woods. She likely saw the elder at the spring scatter the mugwort seeds. She saw plague come to the people, a herald of worse to come. She saw the strangers come and demand land and primacy. She saw the Cayuse fight back. She saw the cavalry ride after Chief Josef and the steadfast Numipu. She saw the people die - of hunger, of disease, of cold, of misery as well as by bullets and bayonets.

She saw the deer and the elk walk their paths still. She watched the wolves, cougars and coyotes trailing them. Owls nested in her trunk and mice among her roots. Miner's lettuce grew thick around her knees in the early springtime.

She saw the people who came down the slope with wagons covered by canvas. She saw them dig the well, hand over hand, bucket by bucket, and build up its walls, stone by stone. She saw them raise children and chickens and goats and cows. They cut many trees to graze their animals, but somehow they missed her. She saw them hungry and tired from working the poor, thin soil of the ridge, not knowing about the camas and biscuit root and the paths of the deer. She saw them bury their children and their elders and straggle away.

And now here I am. I come heartbroken and bruised both body and soul. In the time I was away, I saw war, discrimination for my disability, utter economic failure, a failed marriage, a lost home, children so traumatized by a legacy of racism that they lash out violently at anyone who gets close.

When I look up at her and put my prayers into her branches, I think of all that she has seen. My prayers are not without context. I do think she cares about us and about our modest troubles. She cares, like a grandmother cares, but like a grandmother, she takes the long view. What are my hardships compared to all she has witnessed?

When I tell her my children are struggling, barely surviving because of the harm done to them before they were even born and the harm done in the cold halls of an institution far away, she could show me thousands of children taken from their homes and families. When I tell her I am so tired, my body is broken before my time from hard work and stress and disability, she could show me women carrying burdens far too heavy through deep snow and despair. The land echoes with the spirits of sisters.

I pour out my water bottle on her roots and whisper thanks and comfort. As I turn to go, a branch brushes my cheek and there are three perfect little cones. I understand that these are a gift for me. I take them, feeling the powerful spirit within each one.

From that moment, I strive to be awake. I look to see each being, alive and conscious, each in their own way. It is not easy to pay attention to each person, when you've been taught for years that they are merely things. Many are so much smaller than that grandmother tree or the well or the spring: *A pebble in the hand. The deer trail where I found it. The soil with all its many parts - transformative microbes, powdered minerals, remains of all beings, mitochondria, the messengers of trees. The yarrow stalks picked to aid in the study of the I-Ching, the Book of Changes. The wind. The long shadows stretching out from ridges as the sun goes down.*

I dig camas in the meadow below the spring and biscuit root by the skirts of the Umbrella Tree on the ridge. I harvest the mugwort in midsummer to tie into bundles and I make medicines of St. John's Wort and balsam root. I aim to leave offerings in each place where I harvest, but my brain demands the voices of the human world and too often wanders. The way I know when I have truly connected to a plant person or a stone person is that it feels as unnatural to take from them without reciprocity, acknowledgement and conversation as it would be if I were to borrow salt from a human neighbor without a greeting, thanks or a bit of small talk.

Once I was lonely. I've never fit into the human world all that well with my strange-looking eyes. For a quarter century, I was a foreigner far from home. But now I am surrounded by neighbors and relations. Just like with the human ones, our relationships are complicated and less than perfect. There is sometimes misunderstanding or too long an absence. Yet, this is how relationships heal.

Talis Kimberley

THE GRACE AND THE GIFT

May your beasts go well and thrive
May your walls and roof stand strong
May your well give water clear
And your days be long
May your bones not lack for strength
May your hearth not lack for flame
May your nights be full with rest
And your stores with grain

As the oldest songs are sung
And the oldest tales are told
Shall the year its promise keep
When the wheat turns gold
That the sun once more shall rise
That the rain once more shall fall
And by the grace and gift of both
Shall the wheat stand tall

FIVE BALES HIGH

Half the harvest's undercover
Half the barn's stacked five bales high
What remains lies two fields over
Underneath a clear bright sky
Gather in the fees and favours
Gather in the helping hands
Gather all for winter's keeping
Who are we, if not the land's?

Weather patterns change so quickly
Yesterday 'twas 'five days clear'
Cut and baled a gracious plenty
Hope and faith for one more year
Gather in the willing workers
Gather in the strong of arm
Gather all for winter's keeping
Handfast to the working farm.

So lift the bales and fill the trailer
One more time and sing the last
With songs of longing, love and wonder
Reaching out to touch the past
Gather in the last hay standing
Gather in the weary friends
Gather all for winter's keeping – bring the
Harvest home as Summer ends.

Gather in the fees and favours
Gather in the helping hands
Gather all for winter's keeping
Who are we, if not the land's?

Liz Cruse

HOUSE - AN ECOLOGY

**For Sale: Detached house, two
living rooms, utility room,
kitchen, two bedrooms, one
with en-suite toilet, bathroom.
Downstairs to two further
rooms, bathroom, under stairs
storage space. Centrally
heated. Double glazing
throughout. Small garden.
Parking space at rear.**

The House opens his eyes to the North.

*From a gravelled and Bramble-fringed drive where
the blue VW is parked, the land descends to the Levels.
After heavy rain water lies across the land like sheets of
quicksilver. This land is liminal, remembering that it was
once underwater and then marsh. Solidity does not come
easy to it. There is the Sugar Loaf, one of the rounded hills
that mark the point at which, ten thousand years ago, the
glaciers ceased their progress south and deposited their
load of earth and boulders. Beyond the Levels, the flat
fields where cattle graze, the terrain begins to rise again.
Buildings are scattered across the ascending slope, and
the city of Wells gathers itself on the edge of the Mendips.
On a sunny day the towers of the St. Andrew's Cathedral
and St. Cuthbert's church are visible, tiny building blocks
among the blur of buildings. With his northern eyes he
follows the rise of the Mendips, up to where the telecoms
beacon adorns the highest point with crimson stars of light
at night. And then the sky, clouded, clear, ever-changing.*

She came to inhabit me seven years ago. On a summer day, she reluctantly entered at the urging of an estate agent. I could hear that she wanted an old house, a cosy house with fireplaces, but I knew as soon as she came through my front door that she would work in accord with my soul and embellish me, introduce new beings into me and into my small curtilage. I did my best to whisper welcome to her, to show her my spaces and my aspects, hinting at souls that might inhabit and the vital spirits of things that might feel at home in me.

Not the least of these was her black and white cat. I made a draught blow the cat flap open as she walked past to make the point that in me not only the human mammal was welcome.

I had already been here for some thirty years when she moved in. They built me on a narrow strip of land by the Old Wells Road. A friend gave her a guide book from the 1930s which said the road used to be a Neolithic trackway leading up over what is now called Windmill Hill and down to the valley. Nearby from St Edmund's mound, now hemmed in with houses, on a Winter Solstice morning you can see the sun roll up the slope of the Tor in the distance. So maybe those old people came this way for Ceremony on ancient winter mornings. How can I know? I was not here.

She has a map which shows that a century ago all the land round here was orchard land but the cider apple trees are mostly gone now. A solitary individual stands here and there, beside a road, in a patch of scrub. There are a few old orchards fast falling into decay where Mistletoe weighs down the branches and the trees keel over, old and dying, unable to resist the pressure of cows rubbing up against them. Only their spirits remain, haunting the old map with its tiny, childlike representations of trees in the various parcels of land.

I'm not a beautiful house. My skin is modern red brick. My eyes are glass. Thus Clay and Silica join together in me to keep out the winds and the damp (not altogether successfully in Somerset). My eyes are edged with Plastic, the eldritch resurrection of ancient trees and marine organisms. The sighs of ancient forests blow around me and through me.

But beautiful or not I have become her home. She summoned Wood and Cotton and Wool, furniture, curtains, drapes to join hands to lend me some inner elegance. Feather and Stone and Plant crystallise out of paintings of birds and the demigods and goddesses of seasons of the Earth.

Fired and glazed Clay has settled in my cupboards and on my windowsills. The solid spirit of Iron albeit that he is inclined sometimes to show his red hair and his fancier cousin Steel gleam in me from the kitchen. And Water is my circulation as it is for humans - though you have much added to it in your pipework.

She has assembled Books which hold worlds of words ready for her to release into her mind. Through the air the etheric waves of Electromagnetism compete with the Books to give information and entertainment. So much life here, so many beings, standing and waiting to be of service.

The House opens his eyes to the South.

Here the view is restricted. A small garden is enclosed with railway sleepers that hold back the land that would otherwise slope to the road. There are hedgerow boundaries – mixed remnants of field boundary to the east. Privet stands to the south, Clematis and Honeysuckle loll over a fence to the west. There is Sandstone imported from India. Brick demarcates a flower garden with a pond. It is Winter now, edging into Spring. At this time the garden is quiescent, dead you might say were it not for the cotyledons of wild plants poking up through dead leaves; the daffodils forming their sheathed flower buds; the suspended white moth shapes of a few snowdrops around the little rowan tree. In the summer Sun is fierce, dazzling and blinding through the French windows but now the light is cool. Helios keeps himself shrouded.

When she arrived the sight of the South was dreary: some rotting decking, gravel, the plastic shell of a pond and a tub of Round-up on the wall. She was like a mythical queen with a dragon on her shoulder when she saw that tub of weed killer. The green canister disappeared as if in a swirl of fire, taken to the table for toxic substances at the Dump.

One March day Bumble Bee rummaged into a Comfrey flower at the entrance to the house. She took the visitation as a message that the garden should be for pollinating insects and so it now is.

Within a year, all was changed: Stone where there had been decking; Soil where there had been gravel; everywhere new plants. The plastic pond liner had been buried and filled with water. Newt came out of nowhere it seemed, and Water Snail. So many new beings to keep me company.

The flowers change each year, one making way for another, flighty Cyclamen conceding to Ivy, white Valerian suddenly showing his majestic plumes of green and white. This year an upstart group of Foxglove will raise their spires of thimble flowers. Lady's Mantle replicates its downy inverted parasols of leaves and in the autumn Rudbeckia flowers resplendent in gold and brown. Hover Fly in all his multiplicity dances above them, translating their pheromones into form.

In the hedge border she hangs fat balls and recently a Long Tailed Tit tribe has come morning and evening to flit among the branches and hang two or three at a time feeding so that they may be protected against the cold of night. She welcomes them and they seem unfazed even when she stands close to the feeder.

When a human friend died, she planted Jacob's Ladder - spears of purple flowers. She imagined her friend climbing, weaving his way between the angels to reach the upper worlds. Her picturing hung in the air and I saw it with my southern eyes.

The House opens his eyes to the West.
   If he looks straight ahead there are only houses to see. Humans come and go. They park their cars which leave whiffs of Metal and Petrol. But if the House squints downwards he can see the narrow strip of green that runs along his western edge. In summer Meadow Foxtail and Yorkshire Fog grow tall, eventually going to seed and turning the colour of wheat. There is Clover, red and white. Stridently coloured Ragwort springs up and Cinnabar Moth, crimson and grey, lay eggs which hatch to acid-yellow and black caterpillars. And the house can catch a glimpse of Grapevine, lifeless tendrils now hung with withered grapes, but in October hiding small bunches of sour juicy fruit behind leaves where the yellow shelled Snail also gathers.

She is friendly with the human people but they do not enter me. Bill leans on the railing outside his front door, mournfully speaking into his phone. His wife seldom emerges. Paul mounts his bike ready to ride over the Mendips in his lycra cycling shorts and helmet, balancing against the air, revelling in gravity and friction. Jane and Rob walk their fat and ailing dogs. I watch their slow progress.

   But often, other humans come, friends of hers. I become full of the laughter and bustle of these bipedal creatures. It disturbs my equilibrium and the peace of the other entities is disrupted with clattering and conversation. It is too much to digest. As if sensing my disquiet, Cat becomes skittish, racing up and down the stairs, approaching people then darting away, jumping on the table to demand attention.

   But for two solar cycles Ragwort has played host to Caterpillars. There she pays close and quiet attention, joyful when she sees them, sad that there are not more.

32

Their tiny jaws munch at the leaves until there is only the skeleton of a plant left. Maybe some are at this minute stirring the soup of their cells below the earth down among the grass roots, ready to fly in the summer. She hopes they know she is well inclined towards them.

The House opens his eyes to the East.
Here is a small elevated terrace, a hedge with Hazel, Hawthorn, Privet. Now the catkins, past their best are dangling and swinging in the least breeze. Beyond the hedge six sheep in a field munch and puff and amble over the grass. Some are brown and some dirty cream. Then the sky again. At the Spring Equinox the Sun rises and shines directly into House's Eastern eye. It travels away to the left for the Summer Solstice and then swings back far to the right for the shortest day of Winter. In Summer his eastern eye keeps benign watch over humans sitting reading, talking, eating.

Every day she throws some mealworms onto the roofing felt. Blackbird comes, landing with his graceful tail lift, and Robin flies down – sometimes at the very moment the dried worms patter down. He has been watching and waiting it seems. When there is no food they send silent messages to where she stands behind the windows of the French doors, gazing meaningfully into the house. More nourishment is required. Magpie and her mate have also learned of this source of food and strut around jumping from wall to table. The mealworms are consumed quickly.

She used to hang seed feeders on the wrought-iron balustrade. When she moved in a flock of Sparrow greeted her from the hedgerow making clear their understanding that a human would provide food. Friends gave her seed as a housewarming gift. Sparrows came to the terrace dropping their small feathers at moulting time, bathing in the water dish, chirping and flying in succession to the seed. Blue Tit, Great Tit with their black breast stripe, even a Coal Tit from time to time. There was Dunnock and

Robin. Once a stunned Sparrowhawk swooped in, but missed his prey and clung dazed to the wall for a moment before taking off.

But the cunning and ever vigilant Rat came. She had no animosity towards the one or two that darted out of the privet hedge, seized dropped seed and retreated. But they found my gutters, they found a gap somewhere into my roof space and I confess to unease as they gnawed the rafters (my bones after all) and dragged my soft insulation into nests. Co-existence is not always harmonious or possible; she had them killed. Not without anguish on her part, though I felt some relief.

Now, a few years later, one (at least) is back. She bangs a fierce rhythm on her shamanic drum hoping it will understand her message and that on one of its excursions outside it will meet the silver tabby Cat whom she met one day with a fat rat in its jaw.

The feeders have been moved down to the north eastern corner where recently Starling has come, young and bossy, to maraud the peanuts – though the smaller birds still get their share.

The House closes his eyes.
Now Night has come. Sometimes Moon is visible. Orion, the Plough, Venus, Jupiter, Mars can still be seen despite the street lights, the orange of sodium and the staring white of LED. Blinds are lowered. Curtains are closed. She goes to bed, dislodging Cat from its centre. Kitchen sleeps and makes the occasional drowsy hum. The Computer Screen ceases to shine. The Internet signal is suspended, though unseen, its messages and avatars still hovering in the air. Rat in the roof space runs from one end of the attic to the other. House holds her safe through the sunless hours.

Sally Forth

HOME TRUTHS

I sit on Walla Crag in the nippy freshness of dawn. Tucked into my eyrie on a grassy knoll, I look down at the campsite hundreds of feet below where my family are cosy in their cocoons, where the flapping and snapping oranges, blues, yellows and greens are regaining their colour as the sun rises. The herd of terracotta and cream half-asleep Herefords that had given me barely a glance as I passed Rakefoot Farm are starting to stir. Their sonorous lowing provides the base to the song of the skylarks on the wing. And like an oil bubble in a lava lamp, the amorphous shape of the slate-topped white buildings of Keswick town ebbs and flows across the glowing green pastures to the shores of inky Derwentwater. I pour myself a stream of steaming coffee, but when I add the milk, it is curdled.

I sit on Walla Crag, soothing and placating. I wanted my family to see, to feel, to love this place like I do. But I look at my young daughter's and son's mutinous faces and at their father, a puce sweating ball of irritation. My kids, I know, just wanted to be driven to the Java Cafe in the mediaeval marketplace, to sink into the old brown leather sofas and drink bowl-sized mugs of Belgian hot chocolate with a mountain of marshmallows and cream. And my husband, well, who knows what would make him happy for more than an hour at a time, what would allow a whole day to go by without some ripple of resentment. I have fleshy ridges on the inside of my lips, the result of clamping my mouth shut with my teeth, holding in what I don't want to come out. To offer an opinion, to answer back, to disagree, to show any sign of my own irritation. It's not worth the fall-out, the days of sulky silent treatment that will inevitably follow. "I've brought juice and brownies," I say brightly.

I sit on Walla Crag, picking over that morning's clipped words that nevertheless spoke of a depth of feeling I cannot fathom. The bright blue sky chimes discordantly with my mood, the sunny smiles of the walkers crowding the crag turned into the gape of gargoyles. White-tipped waves blow across the usually calm waters below, surrounded, protected, as they are by the chains of hills I know so well. Stamped across the OS map in bold type is the proud claim CUMBRIAN MOUNTAINS. That makes me smile, for I have climbed vertiginous ancient routes in the Andes and the Himalayas, where majestic peaks reach so high into the breathless stratosphere that the only way to see the full outline, to see the top, is from a hundred miles away. My own heartland shrinks by comparison and yet these hills have a grandeur all of their own. I survey the sharp austere face of Grisedale Pike, and conical Skiddaw which should carry the warning 'tackle my 3054 vertical feet if you dare', and the benign-looking Blencathra, harbourer of the precipitous Sharp Edge that lures in the uninitiated, sometimes to their deaths. I too was lured in, by sweet and funny words that disguised a volcano of insecurities. Nowadays I tread warily, trying to keep away from the edge, from the fire within.

I sit on Walla Crag, laughing with my walking buddies, 'my rocks'. Freya asks Diane if she is ready to operate. Diane belongs in the pages of the book that has become my bible, *The Wilderness Survival Guide.* She is the very essence of 'preparedness' promoted by author Joe O'Leary. Whatever we suddenly need, she has, including the miniature saw I used to cut my bladder's way-too-long drinking tube down to size, while perched on a rocky ledge high up the face of Dale Head. I then discovered I'd had the bladder upside down and so spent the rest of that trip craning my neck backwards to get a drink from the now way-too-short tube. We look across at Skiddaw and remember the muscle-mincing crawl up White Water Dash, followed the next morning by a bushwacking ascent up the back of Blencathra. I lost the skin on the back of my heels. There is a reason we didn't pass another soul, we tease Freya, that weekend's route-planner. As we look over at lofty Grasmoor and gentle Maiden Moor and down through the Jaws of Borrowdale, we begin planning our next girls-getaway. I feel light, happy. And I know. I know it is time for Plan B, the emergency exit strategy Joe O'Leary advises we should always have ready.

I sit on Walla Crag, watching a murmuration of starlings expanding and contracting in the pink and gold of a winter's dusk. I read somewhere that these Continental visitors gather in their thousands to swoop and wheel for communal warmth and to deter attack by the likes of the peregrine falcon, the fastest, most precise hunter on the planet. But the prosaic isn't apparent in this evening's show, only the grace and the wonder. My inner knots unfurl, the tension slides away and my head clears. I start to think about what I need to do next. Get myself a good solicitor is the answer, of course. Did he really think I was that stupid? The single A4 sheet of paper covered in his small, neat handwriting slapped down in front of me on the kitchen bench. It divided up our assets in a way he thought fair, casually disposing of my ability to buy even the smallest of houses anywhere in the catchment for the kids' schools. He handed me a pen, clicking the nib down for an instant signing. I was naive to think we could do this ourselves. That we could somehow waft through divorce and emerge the other end as the very epitome of co-parenting friends. Like in some romantic show that defies reality.

I sit on Walla Crag, pouring my heart out to my soul mate, Amy. We are journalists together and she is already divorced. She is the one person I can talk to with unabashed honesty, sure as I am of her loyalty. I have been hurt by Freya's principled stance that her firmly-married self would take no side. If only she knew how much my almost-ex resents my friends, how much he disdains them all. Unlike the 'other woman' he was shagging before there was even any ink on the page to dry. "Do you know, they came up with the date of November 15th," I tell Amy. "They claim that's when their relationship started, a safe fortnight after our official separation." Our solicitors had finally agreed on October 31st as our own D Day (Detachment Day). But Halloween? Really? Amy raises her hands, "Well …" We laugh and talk some more. She already knows about the sightings of the knacker and his paramour, in late night bars off the beaten track, going back many months now. Going back, I think, to the moment he suspected we were heading for the rocks. He would know. He's been here before. I am his second wife. There's not many places you can hide though when you're married to the chief reporter on the local newspaper. I soon heard the whispers. And felt humiliated. I'm not sure why, because in the end I was the one who called it a day, in an unplanned moment of truth when the words escaped their prison. Amy counsels: "You're hurt because he replaced you so easily. And it's pride - you'll feel better once everyone knows you didn't want the tosser." I stand up stiffly and pull my hypermobile friend up from her perch. God, we've been here for hours. Neither of us had noticed the day fading. We step slowly down the hill for the sake of Amy's knees and go in search of food.

I sit on Walla Crag, sad, relieved. My divorce came through yesterday. The decree absolute arrived in a large white envelope, a flag of surrender, of truce. Twenty years since I floated down the aisle on a cloud of good wishes. Twenty years terminated by unceremonious pro forma. I feel the finality. I wonder if the Countess of Derwentwater, who sought sanctuary here 300 years before me, did too. She must also have questioned, feared, the future as she hid in the forbidding breach below, attempting to escape the King's men hunting down the Jacobite rebels. *Lady's Rake* marks the spot on the OS map, but angry red contour lines warn 'do not follow her!' She did escape that day, but her story ended in a lonely grave, far from home. I know I need to plan, to move forward, to move on, but I am too tired today to make any decisions. I am running on empty. Idly I watch as a flotilla of yachts, white sails hoisted to catch the brisk spring breeze, fan out across the cold waters below. They race and tack and weave between the chain of islands beloved by wild campers and gradually the noise of tumultuous thought fades. I close my eyes, raise my face to the sun and drift.

I sit on Walla Crag, raging. I am so fucking furious, for the first time, I wish you were dead. I wish you'd dropped dead with a convenient heart attack at the right time, at a point when we were still the picture perfect couple, so that I could have been the grieving widow cared for by a compassionate community, the kids and I sitting pretty in the family home, the only home they'd ever known until they were ripped out of it as teenagers. I agreed to sell that house, against my solicitor's advice, so that you would have a deposit to buy another. It seemed only fair. But now you go and do this? You get your own place and then you take mine? As Rachel sat down for breakfast this morning, she said: "Have you seen Dad's Facebook post?" *You proposed to your fucking floozy on top of Walla Crag?*

I sit on Walla Crag with my kids. It is a cold but bright February morning and the date is 01.02.2010. "It's a palindromic date that reads the same backwards as forwards," I tell them. "The last one was in 2001 and before that, way back in the 1300s." Neither of them appears impressed with this rare confluence of day, month and year. But then you never really know what your kids are thinking, what they are absorbing, silently, imperceptibly, like plants drawing in nutrients from the earth they are rooted in. Rachel is 17 now. My mum says she has an old head on young shoulders. She also has a wicked sense of humour. When I originally told her I wanted my ashes to be scattered off Walla Crag, she said: "Sure, I'll do it this weekend". Later, when I recanted, horrified that I might end up mixed for eternity with the remains of my ex and his third wife, she soothed: "Mum, he's 12 years older than you, he'll go before you and he doesn't have the imagination to come up with something he hasn't been able to copy." I smile, but then glance over at Josh, who's 15, checking he hasn't heard, because he still has a good relationship with his dad. But no, he's busy chatting to the young couple sitting sipping from their travel mugs as they survey the scenery. "Starting from the far right, that's Blencathra," I hear him say, "also known as Saddleback because ..." He falters. Rachel obliges: "Because it has two peaks with a plateau in between." Together my kids pan round the landscape, pointing out the hills and some of the places of interest in the valley bottom. There, at the top end of the lake, where the tiny white yachts are moored, that's Derwentwater Marina. "You must go to the marina a little further down though, at Nichol End - it's famous for its ginormous tray-baked scones! But in town, it's just got to be the Java Cafe," says Josh. "You'll know it by the big chocolate fountain in the front window." Rachel can't resist: "And just think, you'll have earned the treat by the time you get there. Isn't that right, Mum?"

I sit on Walla Crag, savouring the internal warmth as I drink my coffee. It is February 2022 and for the first time ever, I have come over to Keswick, to Castlerigg Farm - always Castlerigg Farm - to camp on my own. No tent this time, but a cosy campervan designed for one. Strictly speaking, I'm not alone. My dog Sonny's white woolly body snuggles against mine as I gaze at the peaceful waters of the lake below. I'm not really seeing it. I'm meandering through memories and thinking about how

much has changed since I first began walking these hills.
It is the 22nd today, so 22.02.2022. And I remember the
last palindromic date I sat here, with my kids, when we
were becoming happy again.

Anna Downes

BECOME ONE WITH ALL THINGS

Become one with all things and all beings – visible and invisible good spirits.

Bare foot in the wet sand I stand, knee deep not knowing where the grains and my warm skin begin or end, feeling all the history of every grain that came to be.

Here is now – is me – is all encompassing - mind, body, soul, spirit of this place that is me – all of me – knee deep in wet sand, unable to determine my beginning or ending with this land, this sand from rocks and pebbles ground by crashing waves against a shore – tumbled turned and thrown – rounded, grounded in the sound and air and space – surrounded.

Hear the whole world breathing in and breathing out – cacophony of life – all things and all beings – loud and silent wrapped in the ecstasy of a moment – knee deep - I am the grain of sand brushing against your warm skin. I am the rock that crumbles into the sea, that, crashes with the waves upon your knee, I am the Oyster's pearl – in the tumult of the ocean floor – in the dance – the song – the love – the light – the beacon in the storm.

Lucien Wolf

THEY HAD GROWN FLOWERS

I dreamt as a wishing well and a fishing town,
as wind, as fire, as rain.
I walked under moonlight rays
that glint in spider webs,
between ash and burning and renewal,
and found myself to be childlike.
I wept tears of tar and sap,
I died in clearings and to pointed spears,
I howled as a pack, I opened to swallow villages
to the bottom of my abysses.
I walked on two legs, on four,
as a hundred tiny spines or a thousand spores.
I warmed towards foragers and hunters,
men in fur coats and women with firm cradles,
as they blessed my fingers and chest,
built yurts on my back.
I played for them chirps and warbles,
sprung for them blue bells;
their beauty became my own, their musk
melded with mine.
They left without scarring.
They had thrived wholeheartedly from my gifts.

Quinn Columba
THE REVERSE DRYAD

Once upon a time, there lived a woman. She was not a shepherd, but she lived in a shepherd's hut in a field owned by some kind people who allowed her to live there. The field came right up to the edge of a magical forest that only she could see.

Of course, the forest was there for anyone to see, and *every* forest is magical...but only few have eyes to see it. The woman had eyes to see it. And she knew it was magical for other reasons, too.

She knew it because every day when she walked the forest paths, she felt herself growing younger and younger, until she could laugh and dance, spiraling like a leaf in the air, her heart as light as a feather!

She knew it because sometimes she'd come to a turn in the track with dark upright stones pointing to the canopy, and see the path curving down before her following the sweep of the land into a bowl filled with beautiful yellow-leafed trees. At the very sight, her toes would curl and a charge of longing danced up her spine. It sizzled over her scalp, and down her nose, and settled as a lingering sweetness on the tip of her tongue. And as she gazed, her heart almost burst for love.

She was in *love* with the forest, you see. The forest

44

was in love with her, too. And love is a vast and secret magic.

The forest wooed the woman in the sound of the stream and the scented moist air caressing her face, in the bird-song falling around her and the textures of tree trunks that she would kiss as she passed by. Everything seemed to say '*We love you! You belong! You are part of us*!' Like a song it rose to embrace her from every part of the forest. It coursed through her body, resting at last in the deepest place of her heart.

The woman returned the loving gestures of the forest by walking and touching gently, and by gathering sparingly. And she sang little songs softly to it, while swaying with the trees.

> *"Stone, stream and hillside under your eaves always*
> *dwell within."*
> *I would root into your ground and never leave again."*

In a far part of the forest, a stream descended a stoney ridge with a shushing sound. It filled a narrow channel winding through the forest floor, murmuring demurely among fallen leaves and moss and smooth pale trunks. Some time ago, a tree here had been felled - but not neatly. A tall thin edge of bark and a little wood stuck up taller than the rest. It made a good chair, with a backrest, for the woman to sit on and breathe her love of the forest.

Across from the stump-chair was a tree of great elegance; not very big, but with graceful branches, one of which seemed extended, inviting the woman to sit and stay a while, as good friends do. And this tree was her very good friend.

The woman had heard of dryads - trees whose spirits could take on human form and leave their tree, but would always return to it at last. The woman decided she wanted to be a reverse-dryad; a woman who could take on the form of a tree, and be one for as long as she liked. If she became a woman-tree, she would not need to return to her little shepherd's hut for dinner in the evening. She could remain among her beloved trees instead, drinking water and nutrients from her roots, and sunshine from her leaves.

She would sit thinking this, and imagine her toes extending past her slippers, then rooting into the soft earth near the stream and joining the companionship of the trees who all hold hands beneath the earth. She longed to feel the soft pulse of contact with the others, and sap rising, slow but irresistible in spring to burst into bud and bloom. She longed to sway in wild winds while rain fell and thunder crashed, but stay grounded; held and entwined with her forest love.

Sometimes with her eyes closed, she would imagine so hard that she could feel it - a shift in her heart, a change in her body. And when a gust of wind tossed her hair across her face and she automatically pushed it away…she was surprised at her hand, and that she did not have leaves.

One day on her return to the shepherd's hut, a letter appeared on her blue dutch-door. The kind people were sorry, but the field was being sold, and she would have to move her shepherd's hut. They were glad that at least she still had her home. But the woman shook her head slowly and thought: *If I must leave the forest, I have lost my home.*

She couldn't leave the forest…what would they *do* without each other?

It was already evening, but she wrapped a shawl tight around her. She was no stranger to the forest under moonlight, but even so it could be tricky. This night though, as she found her way through rising mist back to the stream and the stump, she felt even more welcome. Moonlight fell kindly on the path. No root or stone impeded her quick, determined steps, and an owl greeted her softly. The love of the forest rose up around her and drew her deep into its heart. *We love you! You belong! You are part of us!*

At last she settled into her stump-chair and listened to the shushing of the stream while she caught her breath. And then she said aloud, to the stream, the graceful tree, and the whole wide wood: "I love you! I will not leave you!"

And in her heart, she sank deeply into the love of the forest. And her feet sank, deep into the earth....

....and when the light of dawn brushed the tops of the trees, the woman was truly home.

And though there was a search, the kind people and others never found the woman. But the stump by the stream grew a new shoot. And sometimes, a voice seems to echo through the trees, in a soft little song:

"Stone, stream and hillside under your eaves always dwell within,
I would root into your ground and never leave again."

Susanne Mathies

CIRCULAR HIKES FOR MOTORISTS

'Circular hiking trail through the Zausenberger Forst, starting from the Zausentrubel rest stop, length 5.3 km, level of difficulty: easy:

You can easily reach the Zausentrubel service area from Zurich via the eight-lane A3. Leave your car in the car park behind the rest stop. If there is no space left there, you can drive past the converted barn into the underground parking deck which contains another fifty parking spaces.'

The clack of her fingers on the keyboard was the only sound in the parlour of the old forester's house. Granddad had sat here at this desk when he had to report on the forest inventory at the end of the quarter. She had always been allowed to sit there and rummage through his pencil box. On the green desk pad, she could still see the fir tree she had scratched in with a pen as a child.

'Well done, Vreneli!' her grandfather had said. 'You must always cherish the trees, because if the trees die, then all the good in this world will also die.'

But then Granddad had died when Vreni was just fourteen years old. The driver of the SUV was acquitted. At that time she had learned that things did not always turn out right by themselves. Sometimes you had to take things in hand. Later, in reform school, she had learned other useful things.

She straightened her shoulders and continued writing.

'Behind the garden of the service area, follow the wooden sign in the direction of Tannengrund. After about 20 minutes, you will reach a farm track on a hill, which is separated from the hiking trail by a red and white barrier. This barrier was erected to keep riders away. As a hiker, you can safely walk across. Some parts of the path are covered with dense fir branches. Walk on these areas whenever possible to avoid muddy ground.

When you reach the stone bridge in the valley, turn into the narrow path on the right that leads along the stream.

Do not be irritated by the thorny vines. The path is deliberately left untrimmed to minimise disturbance to native wildlife.'

She slapped the return button with her index finger. It was important to give clear instructions. Before she continued writing, she listened briefly to the sounds outside. The wind whistled around the windows and rattled the shutters. The nearby motorway roared in the background.

A bright ringtone from her computer told her that a new email had arrived for the Waldmeister publishing house. She opened the publisher's inbox and read the message.

> 'Subject: *Circular hike through the Niederwald around the Zubeltobel.*
>
> Dear Mr. Waldmeister,
> during our family outing last Sunday, my wife Elisabeth followed your recommendation to climb the embankment at the edge of the ravine to take a look at the cave behind the waterfall. In doing so, she slipped and fell into the ravine. She had to be rescued via helicopter, at a considerable to cost to myself. She is still bed-ridden, and I had to hire a housekeeper. In addition, our dog is traumatized and has taken to barking all night long. I reserve the right to claim damages against your publisher. You'll be hearing from me!
> Anton Gretz'

She stood up and studied the map on the wall. At the lettering 'Zubeltobel' she stuck a pin with a small green fir into the map. It was the third one at this spot.

Then she turned back to her work. She particularly enjoyed this hike.

'At the next bend in the river, change the bank. There are large stones set into the riverbed at intervals that make it easy to cross. On the other side, climb up to the hide to enjoy a panoramic view over the beautiful Zausenberg Forest. The ladder is regularly maintained to ensure hiker safety.'

Again, the bell rang. The new message was marked urgent:

'Subject: *Easy hike over the Krummbuckel glacier for off-roaders.*

Dear Editor,
I'd like to inform you that I'll be taking legal action against your publisher in two matters:
Ad 1)
Contrary to what is stated in your book, the Krummbuckel Glacier does not have a smooth solid surface, but a crack in the middle. My father noticed this when he fell several metres into the rift. Because the edge of the crevasse broke off when I stepped back to get help, he is now buried. The rescue team estimates that he can be dug out by the weekend at the earliest.
Ad 2)
When I returned to the car park, my car had disappeared. The embankment had given way under its weight. So your claim that the car park is specifically suited for off-roaders is false.
See you in court!
Peter Huder'

She smiled as she stuck the pin with the fir tree into the map. This was the first marker for the Krummbuckel glacier.

Slowly she walked to the window and pulled back the curtains. The window panes shook under the gusts of wind. Behind them stretched a bare plain, covered with scrawny grass and peppered with ventilation pipes for the underground parking decks. Once, a dense fir forest had grown here.

She went back to her computer and continued writing.

'From the high seat, walk to the large meadow, and you will already see the service area at the far end. There, the river has a narrow section that even the less athletic can jump without effort. After this easy exercise you have already reached the goal of your little hike.'

Susan Greenwood

A QUEST INTO THE MYTHOLOGICAL DREAMING:
BEING INDIGENOUS AND FINDING INDIGENEITY

The red orange rawness of Arnhem Land in the Northern Territory of Australia seemed to be pulsing with life as I looked out of the aeroplane window on route to Sydney. I felt a sense of deep excitement. It is said that you have to leave home to find yourself, to find what it means to be indigenous, and this was certainly the case for me. Below sinuous rivers, with their tributaries and valleys intersected the Australian land like veins on human flesh, and ancestral song lines, pathways of the mythological Dreaming, held the past within the present. I was on a quest to find out more about this land of the Dreaming, which resonated strongly and had long fascinated me. In the process I would have much to learn about being indigenous.

A few days later, on my eventual arrival in Sydney, a challenge about being indigenous confronted me. Standing in The Rocks, a small museum on the edge of Sydney Harbour, I stared at a copy of an engraving of the Cadigal Aboriginal people by the eighteenth-century poet and artist William Blake. It was strange to encounter a work by Blake, whom I associated with English land through the words of the hymn *Jerusalem*. Blake's work had spoken to me for many years, not least for his famous phrase, 'If the doors of perception were cleansed every thing would appear to man as it is, Infinite'. Blake had never been to Australia, having only left his native London for three years to stay in a cottage at Felpham on the English coast, and I very surprised to encounter his work there. This was intriguing. It seemed to bring my quest for what it meant to be indigenous into sharp relief.

Sydney harbour is dominated by bright gleaming glass windows of the modern buildings reflecting the water lapping at the meeting point between land and sea. Huge tourist cruise ships are moored there like great seafaring sharks after disgorging their passengers, the iconic Sydney Harbour Bridge is in the distance. The brightness of the glass and the sea was a stark contrast to the original sunless buildings that house the Rocks Museum. I felt as though I was in a liminal place between light and dark, it was slightly disorientating. The small museum situated among narrow cobble-lined streets with tall buildings dating from the arrival of the British seemed strangely incongruous in the midst of all the modernity. The British arrival by ships would change what we have come to know as Australia, and here my worlds collided.

The Blake engraving, 'A Family of New South Wales', was copied by him from an original by Governor King. It was published in 1793 by John Hunter, the ship *Sirius*'s captain. This journal recorded in detail all observations of the new land at Port Jackson in Sydney Harbour and Norfolk Island. Hunter wrote about the weather, geological features, and the hostility, or otherwise, of the so-called natives and their interactions. He noted that the natives had dug for yam in this area, and they had fished in the water. William Blake's engraving in the museum showed the Aborigines carrying fishing gear.

This was the start of the British incursion into Australia in 1788. I knew this had been disastrous for the Aborigines, and still has serious repercussions today in terms of displacement from land and culture with its ramifications of alcoholism, petrol sniffing and a 'stolen generation'. William Blake, who never set eyes on any living Aborigines, would nevertheless have been no stranger to issues of colonialization and the cruelties of slavery, having engraved at least sixteen plates that illustrated slave conditions. Blake was an impassioned critique of the industrialisation, mechanisation and rationalisation of his time, thinking that it brought about a problem of Western amnesia, an inability to see that 'everything that lives is holy' among other things. He remained largely optimistic though that 'the sons and daughters of Albion' would 'enlarge their views rather than their investments', and would 'open their minds to the visions in the air'. Blake's main task was to show through his work how to bring about a reintegration of healing of body and spirit through the divine imagination. Could I feel such integration in a land so far from my home, one that felt so very, very different? Could I learn something about what it means to be indigenous?

Wanting to feel the Dreaming, I was searching for something deeper than the pain of appropriation arising from the British invasion, but I couldn't ignore it. I shouldn't ignore it. I wandered along Sydney's harbour seeking a place of connection with this place with its dark Aboriginal history and largely twentieth-century high-rise modern buildings and cruise liners. The glass windows of the harbour buildings glinted and caught the sunlight, such a contrast to the shady, narrow streets of older part of the city of the Rocks Museum. As I looked into the water lapping up the shore right up to the modern city, the sunlight catching the ripples, I could see tiny fish swimming; the fish that the original inhabitants of this land fished. In my imagination time condensed and I felt an affinity with those original Aboriginal people. As I looked up and into one of the glass buildings, a smart restaurant with many tables laid with white tablecloths and cutlery, a man was holding a huge snake that was coiled around his neck. Children, fascinated by the huge creature, surrounded the man. Later this seemed to me to be a magical connection with the water in the harbour and the Rainbow Serpent of the Dreaming mythology, so enigmatic and ubiquitous throughout Australia.

The Rainbow Snake became a trickster; it turned everything upside down in my imagination revealing a different way of seeing and understanding. In that moment I saw Blake's Golgonooza, his mythical city of the imagination, there in the reflections of the glass in the window, as reflected in the sea where the ancient first Aboriginal peoples had fished, and I knew that at some point we were all one. In that moment, everything was united and I understood what Blake was trying to convey when he said that we are all connected in the divine imagination. And then I understood that the Dreaming past is still in the present defying chronological time. But as an anthropologist, I knew it wasn't as simple as that, and that it had to do with being indigenous.

Needing to find out more about how I would feel in relation to this Dreaming land so unfamiliar to me, I participated in a tourist expedition along the song lines deep valley in the Blue Mountains or Colomatta, north of Sydney. The expedition was led by Evan Yanna Muru, an Aboriginal discovery Ranger for the Blue Mountains National Park and Wildlife Service and Aboriginal site officer. Evan was also a member of the Darug Custodian Aborigine Clan, a group formed to bring Darug culture back to life. The Darug were some of the first Aborigines to contact the British, and Evan was keen to pass on Aboriginal knowledge to westerners, who at the end of his expedition he says 'know more than most white Australians'.

The Hawkesbury-Negean River or Dyarubbin that flows through the Blue Mountains, along which the song lines in this area pass, was the first successful frontier between the British settlers and Aboriginals. This place holds ancient time in the present where the Aboriginal ancestors dwell, and has its own creation stories from the Dreaming. There is something about the river flowing in the valley that, '... transcends the everyday and the material, shimmers with mystery and poetry' so much so that poets, storytellers and clever men of settler and Aboriginal societies told of the river's mystical dimensions. The river nurtured the earliest patriotic colonial culture and identity and 'became the last bastion of eighteenth-century ways of life and thinking'; a seedbed for British settler expansion and invasion of Aboriginal lands, a 'crucible' for the colony and nation that followed. However, there was another settler narrative, not so often told. In eighteenth-century Britain the enclosures movements robbed the commoners of their self-sufficiency on common land; they were turned into wage slaves creating unrest as well as poverty and crime. Those convicted of crime were shipped to Australia, but as people living closely with the land they had more in common with Aboriginal culture, more than the British elites would care to admit.

Aboriginal culture is a complex knowledge system that mustn't be generalized, due to the wide variety of local groups, moieties, clans, clan aggregates, dialects, and traditional networks through marriage ties that all define a complex skein of related groups and categories, with many variations in language and tradition. Each person, Evan said, is part of a personal totem determined by the place that the mother was impregnated by spirit, the resulting child being released by a particular ancestor of that place. Increase ceremonies at the site of totem enable the life force, to be released helping the great spirit maintain the source of life. This is a living force recognized through the interconnectedness of the complex kin relationship system with the natural environment connecting all the spirits in that environment – plants, animals, water, air, rocks and soil.

Led by Evan, who was born and bred in the Mountains, down the steep gorge, deep into the valley where the sacred waters flowed, I tried to be aware of my senses, in every footfall attempting to experience something of the Darug Dreaming. During this walk, Evan crouched under a sandstone escarpment once lived in by his ancestors and used for ceremonies, and made a sand painting with his finger to show the interdependence of the cyclical nature of creation through the symbolism of the Rainbow Serpent, which is embodied within everything as a creator spirit. Looking deeper into the reflection of the Dyarubbin waters as they flowed down through the mountainside, I imagined I felt a sense of the Rainbow Serpent, Evan's words about experiencing the Dreaming filtered through my senses. The Dreaming, he said, is entered through an opening of sensory perception and 'just being'; 'the minute you start to think, you're out of the Dreaming'.

Evan pointed out that being connected through the senses and feeling gave the highest level of awareness. This could also be achieved simply through developing sensitivity, feeling through the soles of your feet and directing the imagination to 'see in your mind's eye'. I looked deep into the waters feeling the energy of the Rainbow Serpent, and into the gaps in the rocks, trying to sense deep time, a time that went beneath our cultural differences. I could sense the energy of that in the waters of the Blue Mountains; the water reflections in the sunlight seemed to spark with spitting serpentine spirit.

Touching the eucalypts, whose blue haze gives name to the Blue Mountains, the forest red gums with their bleeding bark, the prickly tea trees, native yams, and white elderberry. I watched kookaburras and cockatoos flying amongst the trees and congregating at the river's meandering confluence of streams. I could feel it as a fuzzy sense of connectedness of all beings.

Coming home to England and the familiar soft rolling green North and South Downs, I knew I'd had an experience that was at once strangely unfamiliar and familiar. The land of the Dreaming was indeed deeply different to my senses in terms of what it looked, sounded and felt like. However, my body felt something I already knew at the same time. Paradoxically, my trip to Australia was indeed a way of coming home, a re-kindling of awareness of indigeneity in my own place of birth, and my sense of fluid multifaceted spirit that flies on wing and swims in rivers much broader and deeper than my own individual being. There was pain, the pain of injustice associated with being indigenous, of the colonial appropriation of Dreaming land, and the seeming indifference to much of its magical heritage to the majority of modern Australia. Despite this, there was something impalpably profound in touching a deep spiritual heritage, one that flows within the streams and rivers, out to a sea of time and space in the human imagination, an imagination not limited to ourselves but shared with all beings. This was a psychic indigeneity that I knew I shared on a cellular, spiritual and interplanetary level. Something deep inside felt resonance, a knowing that somehow, despite all differences, there is sense of participation that connects all in the living, breathing magical eco-system that is our home on our planet Earth. This, I hope, can be a point of communication with all indigenous cultures. For me, it is the true sense of being indigenous, of understanding the pain of separation, and being open to creating a shared space of acceptance of communication. This space for westerners can be summed up once again in Blake's words, 'If the doors of perception were cleansed every thing would appear to man as it is, Infinite'.

Gordon MacLellan

TROLL LANDSCAPE - A CONVERSATION

No matter how hard we may try, or how desperately we may want it, most of us are not and will never become, never qualify (is that the right term?) as indigenous. We haven't got the generations of living in a close and conscious relationship with a place to build the understanding that generally goes with the label. What we can – and maybe should – or could – or ought – to do, is explore our own contemporary sense of a place. There is nothing to stop us building new relationships, opening new conversations, with landscapes, nothing to stop us other than ourselves. We may not live in the same place as our ancestors, we may not live in the place that we feel should be our spiritual home but like any community, one would hope that we could try to get along, to learn from each other, to build a sense of connection with the places and populations where we find ourselves as much as with the other human people around us. For us, as humans, that means learning to listen: putting away our knowing and thinking and believing we've got answers and know what is or should be, and simply listening. Not often to words. More often to the rhythm of a landscape, to the movement of life in a city park, to the wind that blows between buildings. We shouldn't forget where we come from with both family and places, but a conversation between us and our earth-home begins here and now.

59

VOICE 1

Gritstone skin on a stoneface troll, folded down here with grass in the creases of her joints and something scrabbling holes in a nostril. She basks here on the ridge above the Moss, lumpen nose raised to the sun and eyes closed deep in those stone folds. But ravens come and whisper into her sleep, sharpening their beaks on the edge of a finger. In that sleep, she feels the crow who flies by on lazy wings, a curlew's call echoing across the landscape of her dreams. And once in a whole, just now and then, in the slow breathing of a hill-shaped troll, a hen harrier will rest on a head-rock and watch the Moss for movement.

VOICE 2

To sit here and stare
At a rock, a stone, the constant flow of water over the lip, into the pool,
At moss, and fern and fallen leaves,
At this, at that, at bloody everything,
Anything.
It might be you but it's not me.
Me, I'm full of ideas, and friends, and my phone, and memories, and things to do and people to talk to,
Me, I'm full of things to do, and more stuff going on than you can imagine…
All this stopping might be you but
It's not me.
To just sit and,
And…
And…
Stop.

VOICE 3

Stop.
Stop talking and listen,
Stop listening and watch.
Stop watching and feel.
Stone is good.

The curve of a rock face,
The fern in the fold,
The lichen on the edge,
The moss,
Detail.
Don't think. Just look.
Don't look, just feel.
Don't feel, just be,
Touch it. Lean on it,
Lie down on it,
Be warmed by it,
Just be beside it until
Everything
Just
Stops.

VOICE 1
The stream flows
Around, over, running,
Peat brown and frothing,
Knotted roots curl down a hill.
Moss, dragon green,
Golden, stained glass leaves filter light
Filling the space under the branches
With the green stillness of the sea
A rock breaks the beach of leaves, where
Last year's husks lie, dark shells on leaf-mould sand.

VOICE 3
Stare,
Stare.
Then let the staring go.
Just relax.
Feel the stone,
Gritstone warmed by the sun
Limestone polished smooth by centuries of feet and
water,
Don't stare. Don't try.

Don't wait for something special.
Don't expect a significant moment
Stop worrying about "me".

VOICES 1 AND 3
Listen,
Listen to the sound as it falls around you.
Listen with more than your ears,
Listen with all of your self.
Listen until the sounds fills you with birdsong and
whispers.

VOICE 2
Becoming the place where I sit,
Old stone and tree roots,
A grassy heap,
A shadow on a park bench,
I stop trying.
Just sit.
Breathe.

A wind blows round the edges of me,
Me, green as the grass,
Me, brown as the earth,
Bristling beech husks, that's me.
And the river runs through the hollow shape of me.
Here I stop.
Here I let go.
Here I can be still.
Here I become my own troll.

INDIGENOUS

How do we know when those bonds that connect us to place go beyond a straightforward appreciation of a landscape?

Peat water and beaten copper,
Distilled the promise of the hills until
The twisted heather stalks of my nerves,
Are threaded with veins,
Pickled by generations of whisky.

My joy burned out with the heather,
Delight drifting on the smoke,
Withering with scorched fur and scales,
But I am still here,
As skin sifts into sand,
And sand into skin,
And flesh slips into earth.
And clouded skies reflect in clouded eyes,
And I am bound to these hills,
So closely, I can no longer
Separate bone from stone.

The wind blows me away into the evening
And still I return, anchored here
So closely, I can no longer
Separate joy from sorrow.
Here I remain.
While soul,
Soul and spirit dissolve
Into mist and a sunset
Burning long and bright behind northern hills.

Jack Wolf

AFTERWORD

Animist Writing is a tricky thing to categorise – it has strong affinities with Magic Realism, Surrealism, Nature Writing, and the Storytelling traditions of numerous Indigenous and pre-modern European societies, but it does not fit entirely within any one of these, and none of them fits entirely within it. It springs from a world-view in which, as the Anishinaabe thinker and writer Robin Wall Kimmerer suggests, 'the Earth loves you back'.

Unlike most Magic Realist writing – which is inevitably fiction – Animist Writing does not implicitly accept Modernist definitions of 'the real', but seeks instead to offer a reflection of reality from a different perspective. It is, like Animist Thought and Animist Reality, a shifting, fluid thing, whose boundaries are permeable and whose essence is hard to pin down. Nevertheless, some elements do stand out: sometimes, a profound, heartfelt seriousness; at others a playful, even whimsical, tone and approach which often belies a serious subject matter as in Quinn Columba's 'The Reverse Dryad'; or a juxtaposition of seemingly incongruous elements that give rise to a dreamlike atmosphere and to surreal storylines as in Susanne Mathies' cautionary fable 'Circular Hikes for Motorists'. Last – but by no means least – they present an implicit invitation to the reader to reconsider their understanding and assumptions of what 'reality' is that goes beyond the standard Magic Realist demand that the reader 'suspend disbelief'. Even at its most playful, Animist Writing is not a game: it directly challenges the supremacy of 'Modern' ways of thinking and seeing, and refutes interpretations of the material World as a repository of resources fit only for exploitation and the Self as a disconnected individual – promoting instead an alternative view of reality as founded on – even constituted in – reciprocal relationships between both. While it may, sometimes, draw on elements of pre-colonial and pre-industrial thinking and storytelling – and, sometimes, by so doing, become a site of Indigenous resistance – at other times it may actively seek to (re)create a connected mindset through a process of active de-colonisation, by European descendants, of their own world view – as in Susan Greenwood's tale of her encounter with the Aboriginal Dreaming, Liz Cruse's 'House: an Ecology' or Gordon Maclellan's 'Troll Landscape' – or when Ari Farnam talks about her relationship with the well on her parents' land in 'The Ridge'. It may celebrate the closeness of agricultural people to a land to which they have historic ties, as in Talis Kimberley's folk songs 'Five Bales High' and 'The Grace and the Gift', or it may express the immediate and intimate experience of connecting to the Earth beneath one's feet, as in Anna Downes' 'Become One with All Things' or seek to give voice to the land itself as in Lucien Wolf's 'They had Grown Flowers'. But what is really key to any identification and understanding of Animist Writing is the acknowledgement of Intention. Not all Animist creative expression is intended for a readership. Some stories, poems, and songs will be composed extempore and never recorded, let alone published; others will be told regularly, but never written down; while still more, like the art of the Lascaux cave painters, will be meaningful primarily in the act of doing, not the post-hoc seeing or reading.

Any editor or critic who is seriously trying to get to grips with Animist Writing needs to take this intentionality into account; and also to ask whether the work stands on its own as a clear example of the genre, or whether its membership is signposted to any extent by knowledge of the author's biography. There is, I would argue, no need to read Animist Writing according to the principle that biography should be excluded, as there are numerous cases

– Wall Kimmerer being one – where biography and Animist intent are themselves in clear relationship with each other – but author biography alone can never locate a piece of work as Animist. Considering Intent allows the reader to separate one thing from the other, and avoid falling into the trap of assuming that all Indigenous Writing must employ an Animist viewpoint, and all Euro-descendant or Settler writing a Modernist one.

There is a difference between being Indigenous and becoming indigenous. The first is an identity – Anishinaabe, perhaps, or Saami, or San Bushman. The second is an intention, a desire, and an ability to weave yourself into the web of being that surrounds you. Wall Kimmerer, again, puts this neatly in her discussion of the little plant she calls 'White Man's Footsteps' – while it may not have been native, it has naturalised, establishing its own ecological niche without causing damage or destruction to any other. It knows that it is staying. It has done exactly what we need to do – all of us, whether we live in the lands of our ancestors, or have travelled to a new place which does not (yet) know us, or are still wandering, still looking for that special place where we will feel that we have finally come home. Like Sally Forth, in 'Home Truths', who tells us of how the relationship she developed with one single place sustained her through a hard time in her life, we need to forge those relationships with both wider Place and individual places that will sustain us and the land itself through tricky times ahead. We need to become indigenous: to weave ourselves back within the web of relationships; to come home to the Earth – which is, after all the only home we have; and to decide that we are staying home.

EQUINOCTIAL HORSES

Seven days after the World Wide Web went down
One last time, and the airwaves fell as silent as the past,
They manifested out of nowhere, in the stubble field
Beneath the mobile mast. Four horses.
Lame, exhausted, broken-winded things:
The four sway-backed old nags of the Apocalypse.
We didn't know what to do with them. We had
No stabling left, no paddocks, nowhere
We might sensibly pasture four dying horses.
We discussed getting the shotgun. But then
Where and how ought we to have concealed
The carcasses of four apocalyptic steeds?
In the end we did nothing at all. We left
The gate wide open and the stubble unploughed.
It was the twenty-second of September.

The next day was the first, and after that the lengthening
Nights brought on the pains of winter, sloshing rains
And sleet that turned the world to mire. The horses
Stayed right where we'd found them, shoeless in the mud,
Ignored the open gate, the road beyond. Each day we
Struggled through the barren clag to see if they had gone,
But they had claimed the field; it soon began to seem
As if the soil answered to them instead of us. Somebody
Said we ought to chase them out, but Nobody
Dared be the one to do it, so the change
Became a steady state, established and incontrovertible.
After a while our interest in them waned, and

HOMECOMING

We stopped going out to check. We just assumed
They were still there: four horses inconveniently
Manifested out of nowhere. Mid-November

The old mobile mast began to rust. We were surprised,
Because the mast had always seemed to us invincible.
We went back into the field, we circled round it,
While the horses stood foursquare, watching us
Out of half-blind sunken eyes as we danced round
And round the rotting metal. We could not tell at all
What they were thinking. One of them
Was chestnut red, tall as a warhorse and his flanks
Flecked with white hairs where spurs had dug
Into his sides: the unmistakable scars
Of appalling horsemanship. We imagined
We could see old battles playing
In his eyes, their liquid sheen reflecting
Back to us a sort of Armistice.
We thought about the shotgun, but again

None of us dared to fetch it. By Midwinter, the mast had
Fallen down. But still the horses stayed,
Inevitable, inexplicable. When we went back
In February to re-seed the field, we could no longer tell
It from the wilderness: only the steel gate left open
To the road reminded us where it had been. If the four
Horses were still there they were too well concealed
Behind the thickening alder and young willow scrub
For us to see them. We did not try enter,
Dragged our plough home, left the land alone to its
New masters. It seemed only right. By May,
Even the gate had rusted off its hinges,
Brambles growing chest high between the posts.

We nipped the young buds off the hawthorn boughs,
Picked garlic mustard, nettles, horse mushrooms.

Seemed only right. The light came back as spring
Expanded into summer. We stopped asking one another
     where
The world had gone: the Web, the mast, the gate.
Forgot the shotgun. We'd no bullets left now Anyway, nor
Skill or means of making any more.
We left it broken by the far wall, propped up on
An empty crate that had been used for apples. By
Midsummer, the gun had disappeared. We knew
This was a good thing. One day, we thought
We heard hooves coming closer, thought
We saw the horses walking slowly down the lane. The
Red was leading, three greys shuffling behind: Sway-
Backed, lame, exhausted, broken winded things. We
Didn't dare to blink in case we missed them.
Afterwards, we couldn't be sure they'd been there at all.

Autumn brought other worries: wild October winds
Heralded flooding, the cold Spring had
Choked off the apple crop. We kept a close eye on
Our stacked supplies of firewood, cut
Into our cords of oak and blighted ash,
Still good enough to burn, if not to sell.
It made no odds: no-one'd had any money since the day
The air fell silent. The leaves lay where they'd dropped
Along the lane. The brambles in the empty gateway
Thronged with fieldfares. One day we ran out of matches,
But at least by then we'd relearned the old ways
Of flint and tinder. We set snares in the hedgerows.

70

Wild rabbits found their ways into our gardens
And our cooking pots. We started making plans.
We wove a white bowl out of willow stems. We gathered.

LIST OF CONTRIBUTORS:

GRAHAM HARVEY is emeritus professor of religious studies at The Open University, UK. He has researched with Jews, Pagans and Indigenous peoples. Most of his recent work has engaged with "the new animism". He lives in Northumberland and has recently taken on an allotment in an effort to discover what "retirement" means.

BETH MANN 'A native of South West England, I moved to south western Spain three years ago and have been seeking a connection to this land ever since. I graduated from Bath Spa University's MA in Creative Writing in 2015, and my short stories have been published in the interdisciplinary journal 'Revenant' and 'Timeless Tales Magazine'.'

ARIE FARNAM is from the Blue Mountains of Oregon. She returned here after 23 years as a newspaper correspondent in Eastern Europe. Her publications include the dystopian *Kyrennei Series* and *The Children's Wheel of the Year*. She mentors fellow writers, blogs at www.ariefarnam.com and pursues studies as a Druid.

TALIS KIMBERLEY is a prolific Wiltshire-based songwriter whose work is inspired by folklore, history, and our relationship with the land. Her eclectic faith-path is at the heart of all her writing. A fiddler-for-morris and a crafter besides, Talis performs widely with guitar and concertina, sharing story-songs with warmth and humour. www.talis.net

LIZ CRUSE is a Druid. Her commitment to protecting the land and fostering connection with all beings underpins her practice as Storyteller, Writer and Poet. She has contributed to Hot Poets – most recently in *Sparks* (2022). She works on an organic farm and runs workshops with older women. She lives in Glastonbury with her cat, Sam.

SALLY FORTH A journalist by trade and a country bumpkin at heart, Sally Forth is fascinated by human psychology, particularly our relationships with each other and the natural world. That, and the rich history of her native Tyneside, is the inspiration for much of her work. She is currently doing an MA in creative writing at Newcastle University.

ANNA DOWNES 'I live in the Valleys of South East Wales. I retired from being a special needs teacher in further education 6 years ago because of osteoarthritis. I am 65 years old this year, and have been a member of OBOD, Bardic Grade for 2 years. I have always written poetry since winning an Eisteddfod competition in my school at the tender age of 11. Now, sitting in my garden looking out over an amazing panoramic view, I am blessed with the inspiration to write of nature and the natural world around me.'

LUCIEN WOLF is a 20 year old physics student at Leeds University with an all-encompassing drive for anything artistic or vaguely interesting, and a strong belief in the inherent divinity found at the centre of reality. He says this bio may be the most pretentious thing he has ever written, but still stands by it.

QUINN COLUMBA (she/her) is a neurodivergent empty-nester remembering how to daydream, dance and say what she thinks. A really good day involves exploring embodied mystic paths and listening to the Diggy Diggy Hole song (Wind Rose version). She lives in a magical

73

cliff-side cottage with her differently-abled husband of 30 years. Her fantasy novel *The Elementist* is currently in revision. ladyquinn.enchantress.earth

SUSANNE MATHIES was born in Hamburg, and holds a PhD in economics and in philosophy. She has been living, writing and painting in Zurich for many years. Five of her German language crime novels have been published to date, most recently *Mord im Lesesaal,* 2021, and *Mord mit Limmatblick,* 2022, both at Gmeiner Verlag, Messkirch, Germany.

SUSAN GREENWOOD has a PhD in anthropology from Goldsmiths College, where she was a Lecturer on the anthropology of religion. She has also taught courses on Shamanic Consciousness and Altered States of Consciousness at the University of Sussex. More information can be found on susangreenwood.org.

GORDON MACLELLAN is a writer, poet and storyteller whose work explores the relationships between people, places, passion and wildlife. As Creeping Toad, he works with community groups to find ways of celebrating those relationships. Other writings include *Old Stones and Ancient Bones* (poems, direct from Gordon) and *Sacred Animals* (Green Magic Books, 2023) Find out more: creepingtoad.blogspot.com / Social media: creeping toad

JACK WOLF is a writer and academic whose first novel *The Tale of Raw Head and Bloody Bones* (Chatto and Windus / Vintage) was published to critical acclaim in 2013. Jack set up Aurochs Underground Press in 2022 in response to the urgent need to re-evaluate human relationships to one another and the Earth itself. Jack's second novel, *Mammoth and Crow*, was published by AUP in 2022, along with a poetry collection, *Dog Walking*

74

Weather. To find out more visit: Aurochspress.co.uk

MARIA STRUTZ is an artist, printmaker, sculptor and translator of various subjects. She has an online shop at https://maria-strutz.onlineweb.shop/ 'At the core of my art is a strong connection to nature; the spirits of animals and plants, landscape, stones, the sea and the elements. My art is about pattern recognition, weaving dreams, stories and images into a whole.'

CARRIE OSBORNE 'I have a lifelong love of drawing focusing particularly on themes of nature, mythology and the human figure. I explore my responses to the natural world through both images and prose poetry, using mainly pen & ink, watercolour and more recently relief printmaking. 'Shield Maiden' is an original linocut from a series called 'Ancestors' exploring the threads reaching back and rooting us to our origins.' Facebook: @CarrieWordhoardsArt

NOTE

Where contributors are based in the US, Canada or other countries where US spelling and punctuation rules are commonly used, these have been retained in accordance with the localist ethos of Animist practise.